CLASSIC LANDFORMS OF THE
SUSSEX COAST

This guide is dedicated to my sixth form students;
I hope it helps.

Rodney Castleden

Speak now, and I will answer;
How shall I help you, say;
Ere to the wind's twelve quarters
I take my endless way.

A. E. Housman

CLASSIC LANDFORMS OF THE

SUSSEX COAST

RODNEY CASTLEDEN
Roedean School, Brighton

Series editors
Rodney Castleden and Christopher Green

Published by the Geographical Association
in conjunction with the
British Geomorphological Research Group

THE GEOGRAPHICAL ASSOCIATION

PREFACE

Some elements in the landscape we see around us are very ancient; some change very rapidly, almost while we watch. Landscape scientists (geomorphologists) can explain these landforms, and the processes that make them, but much of their work is published in specialist journals and is therefore not available to the general public. It is one of the aims of this book to make explanations of the most striking and interesting landforms in England and Wales accessible to all. These classic landforms are naturally of interest to geography students, both in school and university, and we hope that the style and format of this series of guides will make them easy to use both at home and in the field. We hope that a clearer understanding of the origins and dynamics of landform development through time and space will help both student and visitor to maximise their appreciation and enjoyment of the landscape.

Encouraged by the response to the first edition of the Classic Landform Guide Series we are pleased to introduce this new edition. This guide to the landforms of the Sussex Coast includes new sections on Pagham Harbour, Langney Point and Dungeness, a discussion of fossil landforms now submerged on the seabed and the implications of recent archaeological finds at Hope Gap and Boxgrove, as well as updated interpretations of the raised beaches, which are now thought to be older and more complex in origin than before. These improvements will, we hope, make this guide significantly more useful.

This new edition also benefits from the valuable support of the Ordnance Survey Education Team, who have very kindly permitted us to use extracts from the relevant Ordnance Survey 1:50 000 series.

The relevant maps for the area covered in this book are the Ordnance Survey 1:50 000 Landranger sheets 189, 197, 198, and 199; please refer to the current Ordnance Survey Index for 1:25 000 availability.

Rodney Castleden *Roedean School, Brighton*
Christopher Green *Royal Holloway, University of London*

ISBN 1 899085 17 3

This edition first published 1996

Published by the Geographical Association, 343 Fulwood Road, Sheffield S10 3
The views expressed in this publication are those of the author and do not necess represent those of the Geographical Association.
The Geographical Association is a registered charity no. 313129

CONTENTS

over photograph: Sea-cliff at Castle Hill, Newhaven. Woolwich Beds are seen
rest unconformably on Upper Chalk. This is the only natural exposure of the
basal bed of the Sussex Palaeogene, the 'Reading Bottom Bed' (dark brown
layer), a marine flint pebble bed. *Photo:* Rodney Castleden

Frontispiece: Beachy Head. *Photo:* Eastbourne Borough Council

pping reproduced from Ordnance Survey 1:50 000 Landranger mapping with the
permission of The Controller of Her Majesty's Stationery Office
©Crown Copyright 82324M 09/96

Copy editing: Sue Martin

Illustrations: Paul Coles

Series design concept: Quarto Design, Huddersfield

Design and typesetting: Armitage Typo/Graphics, Huddersfield

Printed and bound in Hong Kong by Colorcraft Limited

INTRODUCTION

Visitors exploring the Sussex coast are invariably impressed by the wide range of landforms they discover. This book describes and explains some of the most accessible and interesting sites, which have been selected to give an insight into the development of the coastline as a whole. Compared with inland terrains, coasts change rapidly. The Sussex coast is exceptionally dynamic, with the fastest rates of both erosion and accretion in the south of England. The superb and dramatic visual contrasts in the scenery of the Sussex coast are a direct expression of the processes working towards these dynamic extremes.

Parts of the crenellated coastline produced by the postglacial sea level rise have been preserved in the west: Chichester and Pagham Harbours are sheltered from wave attack by the Isle of Wight and the one-time Isle of Selsey, and have no large sediment-laden rivers emptying into them.

Further east, a combination of erosion and deposition has produced an unusually straight coastline. As the straightness plot shows, long stretches of the Sussex coast are almost dead straight and the county coastline as a whole from the Witterings to Rye Bay, i.e. leaving out Chichester Harbour, is only 23% longer than a straight west-east line 125km long.

Average tidal range west of Selsey Bill is 3m, rising to 4m at Pagham and 6m at Eastbourne, remaining at that level until beyond Dungeness. Such a large range is likely to be inimical to the development of spits, but there has certainly been spit development in historic times at Pagham and Shoreham Harbours, Langney Point, Winchelsea and Dungeness. The hostility of the environment to spit-building may explain why shingle barriers were formed across bays and ria entrances relatively late. The large tidal range is similarly hostile to the formation of deltas, yet one feebly developed **cuspate delta** does exist at Cuckmere Haven.

There is another paradox. The overall tendency for beach sediment to move eastwards has invariably been attributed to **longshore drift,** but there is little evidence that longshore drift is of more than local importance. Even the relatively open bays of the south coast of England, such as Cuckmere Haven or Brighton Bay, may be closed systems, supplied with beach sediment only by onshore wave action as sea level rose at the opening of the present **interglacial** (about 8000 BC), and thereafter more or less cut off from marine sediment supply from outside.

The long distance, long-term migration of sediment may be explained better in relation to the large-scale variations in sea level that accompany climatic changes. In warm stages the sea is at its present level or a little higher: in cold stages it drops 100-140m, leaving the eastern Channel floor exposed as a plain. When sea level is low, solifluction and summer streamflow redistribute the stranded beach sediment across this plain: some is carried by streams down-Channel along the northern palaeovalley (Figure 9). When the sea rises again at the onset of a new warm stage, that movement goes into reverse: the invading sea floods the lower reaches of the palaeovalley first, its waves combing sediment back up-Channel, finally bulldozing it into offshore bars and confining it in bayhead

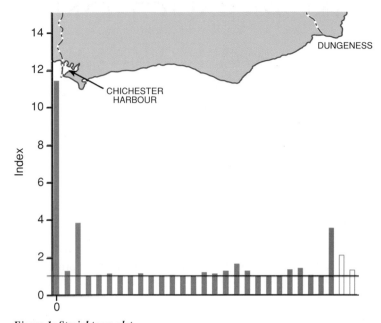

Figure 1: Straightness plot

*The coastline as measured at high water mark on 1:50 000 maps, in 5km legs,
northing to northing. An index of 1.00 would mean a dead straight west-east coast.
Note that, Chichester Harbour and Dungeness apart, this coastline is very straight*

beaches. Computer-generated models of tidal currents in 7000 BC, when
the sea level was at –25m, clearly indicate that sediment was then being
vigorously swept eastwards across the seabed from Dorset towards the
then very narrow Dover Strait (Austin 1991): this movement was much
stronger before the slight tidal changes accompanying the postglacial sea
level rise. The overall distances travelled by beach sediment in these
100 000 year cycles may be very great, although the net result may appear
to be no more than bay-hopping. Current longshore drift may be
responsible only for local shaping and retouching of bars and beaches,
with **onshore drift** the dominant process through at least the first half of
each interglacial.

The processes are rapid enough for large-scale changes in coastline
shape to have taken place in historic times, and our understanding of local
history is enhanced by a knowledge of the ways in which the coastline
has evolved. Accretion in the inlets, for example, helps to explain the
decline of once important ports such as Pevensey or Seaford and the
failure of the medieval new towns of New Winchelsea and Wardur.
Catastrophic loss through marine erosion explains the total disappearance
of numerous settlements such as the early medieval villages of Ilsham
near Middleton, Cudlowe and Atherington near Littlehampton and Pende
near Lancing. Old Winchelsea and Old Brighthelmstone were lost to the
waves; Selsey remains, deprived of its deer park, monastery and
cathedral: it is with Selsey, a classic meeting ground for historical
geographers and students of landforms, that we begin.

SELSEY BILL AND PAGHAM HARBOUR

Selsey Bill

The flat headland of Selsey marks the widest development of the coastal plain separating the South Downs from the sea throughout West Sussex. The solid geology of the plain comprises mainly Palaeogene sands and clays (see Table 1): major elongated inliers of Middle and Upper Chalk stretching from Emsworth to Littlehampton are produced by an upfold, the Littlehampton Anticline. The remarkable flatness of the coastal plain is **discordant** with the geological structure and, as a result, between West Wittering and Selsey Bill the shoreline is eroded across no less than 39 consecutive beds in three geological formations (Wittering, Earnley and Selsey). It seems that the crest of the **anticline** was trimmed to its present form during transgression and regression of the sea either in the last interglacial (**Ipswichian** = Oxygen Isotope (OI) Stage 5e) or in earlier interglacials (see Table 2 on page 12). The plain may therefore be thought of as a remnant of a broad **shore platform** which rises gradually to a cliffline along the foot of the South Downs **back slope** (Figure 2). The ancient sea cliffs, originally 10m high in places, have been buried under later superficial deposits so that they are no longer visible as surface features.

The old shore platform is coated with layers of sand and pebbles (Figure 3) left by the sea as it retreated from its high, interglacial shoreline, but a problem in interpretation is created by the large height range of the beach material: it has been observed at altitudes ranging from 2m to 14m above present sea level, an unusually large range for a single beach, it would seem. The question is discussed in the section on Black +where a remnant of what may be the same **raised beach** is exposed. Here it is sufficient to suggest that possibly sea leve‚l varied significantly within the Ipswichian warm stage, enabling beach material to accumulate as high as 14m OD.

The ancient cliffline and the northern edge of the beach deposit are covered by spreads of **coombe rock,** a chalk sludge produced by alternate freezing and thawing under cold climate conditions, probably during the **Devensian** cold stage. On top of the coombe rock or, further south, resting directly on the beach deposit, is a layer of fine brickearth. This too was probably deposited during the Devensian cold stage, originating as a wind-blown **loess** swept southwards across the tundra by winds from the margins of the ice sheets that covered northern Britain and Scandinavia. Once deposited on the Sussex coastal plain, the brickearth

Table 1: Geological formations of the Sussex coast – a chronological table

Period		Beginning (MYBP)	Rock formation	Maximum thickness (m)
Pleistocene		2.5	Raised Beaches, Brickearth, Coombe Rock, Terrace Gravels	20
Neogene	Pliocene	7	-	-
	Miocene	23	-	-
Palaeogene	Oligocene	35	Silcrete (sarsen stones)	1
	Eocene	53	Bracklesham Beds	180
			London Clay	60
	Palaeocene	65	Oldhaven and Blackheath Beds	-
			Woolwich and Reading Beds	9
			Thanet Sands	-
Upper Cretaceous			Upper Chalk	240
			Middle Chalk	73
			Lower Chalk	80
Lower Cretaceous		135	Upper Greensand	60
			Folkestone Beds[1]	
			Sandgate Beds[1]	
			Bargate Beds[1]	200
			Hythe Beds[1]	
			Atherfield Clay[1]	
			Weald Clay	480
			Tunbridge Wells Sands	120
			Wadhurst Clay	70
			Ashdown Beds	210

[1] Often grouped together as Lower Greensand

was locally reworked by streams flowing during the brief summer thaws and solifluction. At Selsey the brickearth is a virtually stone-free loam with a few mammoth bones, some of them water-rolled, giving an indication of the Arctic ecosystem of the brickearth phase. It also contains a few flat pebbles of Triassic quartzite similar to those found on Chesil Beach in Dorset; these may well have arrived stepwise from Dorset, by means of alternate **periglacial** river transport out onto the Channel floor and onshore combing-up movements associated with the waves of rising interglacial seas.

At Selsey Bill, modern marine erosion has exposed the superficial deposits and a close study of them has revealed complex environmental changes during the period of deposition. The ancient shore platform on

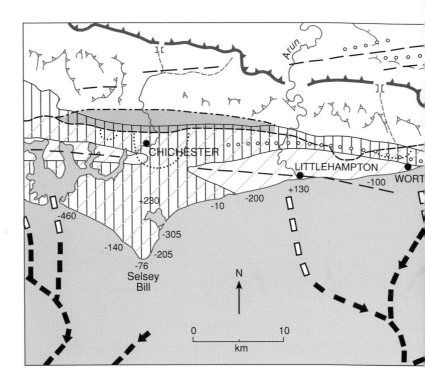

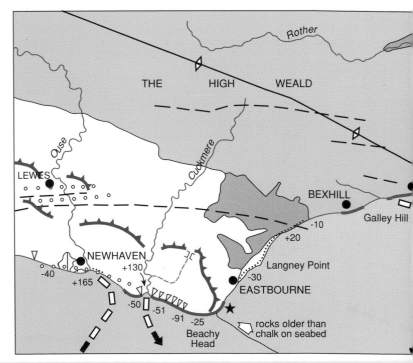

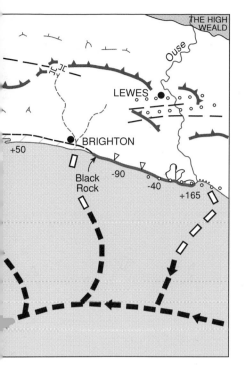

Figure 2: Morphological map of West Sussex

⊥⊥	Lower Greensand escarpment
▲▲▲	Main Chalk escarpment
△△	Secondary Chalk escarpment
⊨	Windgap
----	Principal dry valley
······	Coombe Rock fan
---	Upper raised beach complex and cliffline
---	Lower raised beach complex and cliffline
⊞	Palaeogene rocks
⬇⬇	Devensian extension of river across seabed (black, proven channels, white, inferred course)
— —	Axis of anticline
o o o o	Axis of syncline
�	Main alluvial deposit
········	Major shingle deposit
—	Low cliff
▬▬	Cliff over 8m high
⊞⊞	Abandoned Flandrian cliffline
▽	Hanging dry valley
▼	Hanging stream valley
★	Landslip complex
◆	Wealden tectonic divide
-10	Mean annual erosion rate in cm over the last century
+10	Mean annual accretion rate in cm over the last century

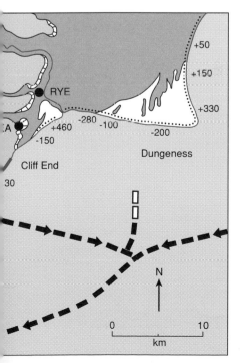

Figure 3: Morphological map of East Sussex

Table 2: Middle-late Pleistocene on the Sussex coast

Climate	Oxygen Isotope stage	Stage name	Age in 1000s of years BP	Landscape process
W[1]	1	Flandrian	0-10	Floodplain alluvium deposited; silting of bays
C[2]	2			
W	3		40	Erosion of floodplain basements; periglacial conditions; low river terraces (e.g. Arun 1-4); activation of Chalk dry valleys
C	4			
W	5a	Devensian	60	
C	5b			
W	5c		90	
C	5d			
W	5e	Ipswichian	125	Selsey and Black Rock raised beaches retouched?
C	6			Periglacial conditions (Arun 5?)
W	7		210	Selsey and Black Rock raised beaches?
C	8			Periglacial conditions (Arun 6?)
W	9	Hoxnian	330	
C	10			
W	11		410	
C	12	Anglian	450	
W	13	Cromerian	490	Goodwood, Slindon and Boxgrove raised beaches
C	14			
W	15		560	

1. Warm or temperate climate. In warm stages like the present Flandrian stage the following processes predominate: desiccation of dry valleys; fluvial reworking of loess; temperate rivers, mainly single-channel and meandering, stable or gently downcutting; high sea level, i.e. close to present level; drowning of lower reaches of drainage networks; initial formation of highly indented shoreline.
2. Cold or periglacial climate in which the following processes predominate: intermittent (seasonal) activation of dry valleys; solifluction; formation of coombe rock and loess; nival, braided rivers forming fluvioperiglacial pediments; low sea level; extension of drainage networks across the Channel floor,

which the raised beach deposits rest is dissected by channels containing pockets of silt. Fossil snails show that the silt now 2-3m below sea level was deposited under freshwater conditions; at 1.8m below present sea level and above, the conditions were estuarine: this shows that sea level was rising. Pollen from the upper level indicates that park tundra gave way to mixed woodland with oak and hazel dominant, and proves that the sea level rise associated with the deposition of the overlying sand and pebble bed was indeed connected with a major climatic improvement, the onset of an interglacial, thought to be the Ipswichian.

The channels in the Ipswichian shore platform nevertheless create a further problem because they imply an episode of stream erosion separating the formation of the shore platform and the deposition of the overlying beach sediment. This is the kind of evidence that has led some geomorphologists to propose that the platform was originally cut at an earlier date than the Ipswichian: it is possible that only local retouching occurred when the Ipswichian beach material was deposited. It is even possible that the southerly parts of the shore platform were planed off by wave action during the stage 7 interglacial, while the higher northern parts of the platform were eroded later in stage 5e (the Ipswichian): there is no reason why Ipswichian sediment should not rest on a platform of stage 7 age.

In the 1960s, temperate peat and freshwater stream deposits near the lifeboat station (SZ 862927) yielded remains of frogs and beavers and the almost complete skeletons of a straight tusked elephant (*Palaeoxodon*) and a rhinoceros-like animal *(Dicerorhinus)*. These deposits were attributed to the Ipswichian interglacial. Amongst the elephant bones were two flint tools, showing that palaeolithic people had either hunted this large animal or scavenged its corpse. Sea defences and the resulting accumulation of beach sediment mean that unfortunately these fascinating deposits can now rarely be seen.

The modern shore platform at Selsey and to the west is of geological interest because it exposes the Bracklesham Beds, containing a rich variety, over 500 species, of Eocene marine fossils. The best time to look for these is at low tide, near the low water mark. There are also **erratic** boulders resting on the platform, stones including Bembridge limestone from the Isle of Wight and granite from the Channel Islands, which could not have reached Selsey by 'constant sea level' processes such as longshore drift. Introduction by an enormous ice sheet advancing up the Channel was suggested in the 1970s but has not been widely accepted. Transport by ice floes or bergs during a cold stage is a more popular explanation, although the association of full glacial conditions with low sea levels would seem to argue against it. It may be that this apparent contradiction can be resolved; if sea levels have gradually 'stepped down' during the Ice Age some of the early cold stage low sea levels could easily coincide with the higher levels of later warm stages, including the present interglacial. On the other hand, geomorphologists are currently tending to favour the idea that sea level is more or less *constant* aside from **glacio-eustatic oscillations,** so we must consider another possibility: that cold conditions set in very rapidly at the start of a cold stage, creating glaciers and ice caps in the north and sending icebergs to the south coast of Britain while the sea level was still high. Sir Charles Lyell noted that erratics found on Arctic beaches are sometimes transported in the roots of floating tree trunks: perhaps this 'periglacial' explanation from the mid-nineteenth century may be revived.

The Selsey erratics include Bembridge limestone, large chalk flints, sarsen and Upper Greensand chert originating in the Isle of Wight, angular boulders of a grey sandy clay from the Bognor Rocks 10km to the north-east and numerous rounded cobbles that seem to have come from the West Country, Brittany and the Channel Islands (diorite, felsite, greenstone and granite). This material need not have travelled far in the present interglacial; the Selsey raised beach also contains erratic material and may currently be supplying the foreshore with recycled exotic rock specimens: if so, the erratics were brought into the Selsey area in the distant past, in the Ipswichian or earlier. Students hunting for erratics should be cautious. A century ago, when some erratics were pointed out to him on the foreshore at Medmerry, Thomas Woodland replied that they were 'the remains of our rick-steddles, to keep the rats off: this is where our rickyard was.' The possibility of human interference is ever-present.

Selsey Bill is made of soft sands and clays capped by unconsolidated layers of pebbles and silt; it is remarkable that a headland composed of such soft materials can exist. The Bill itself is protected form the worst effects of wave attack by the Mixon Rock, a reef of hard shelly limestone 2km to the south (Figure 4). Over a long period the villagers of Selsey visited the

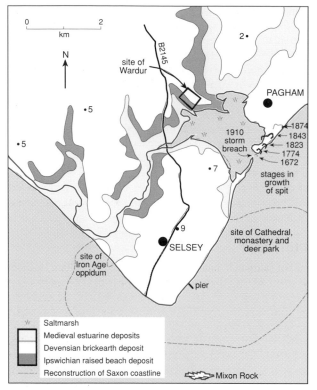

Figure 4: Selsey Bill and Pagham Harbour

Mixon Rock at low tide to quarry building stone for their cottages, but in about 1820 the Admiralty banned further quarrying because the anchorage on the east side of Selsey Bill was deteriorating. Manor Farm at Nyetimber is built of waterworn cobbles of Mixon Rock laid in a characteristically Saxon herringbone pattern: this use of the stone may date from the eighth or ninth century AD, so the reduction of the natural breakwater of the Mixon Rock went on for many centuries before it was stopped.

The south-west facing coast, though exposed to waves driven by the dominant winds, is given some protection by the very gentle gradient of the seabed offshore: many waves slow, break and spend their energy before they reach the beach. Nevertheless, 6km along to the north-west, at Bracklesham, a strip of coastline 277m wide was lost to the sea between 1780 and 1875, a mean loss rate of 2.9m per year. Taking the Bill itself, it is the eastern flank which has the fastest erosion rate: the cliffline north-east of the lifeboat station has retreated at an average rate of 2-3m per year over the last hundred years. These are the highest medium-term (100-year) rates of erosion along the Sussex coast, with the isolated exception of West Wittering, where the cliffs have retreated at an average of 4.6m per year. Short-term (20-year) erosion rates can be still higher: up to 6m per year between 1932 and 1951.

The rates of erosion at Selsey are lower than might be expected, given its low relief, unresistant geology and exposure to strong winds. The shallowness of the sea on all sides plays a part: indeed the role of the offshore zone in shoreline processes is often underestimated. A line of reefs, shoals or shallows girdles the Bill about 7km from the shore. Some of these shoals, known collectively as 'The Owers' (possibly deriving from the Saxon ora, meaning shore, which this may have been in the Saxon period), are only 0.6m below the low water mark. They absorb significant amounts of wave energy.

In the Iron Age and Anglo-Saxon period large areas of these shallows were above sea level, forming a broad, hammer-headed foreland (Figure 4). The loss of this substantial land area, due to a combined attack by waves and **piddocks** (which have riddled with holes all the Milioline limestone reefs on each side of the Mixon Rock), led directly to the abandonment of Selsey Cathedral in 1091 and the building of a new cathedral at Chichester.

Pagham Harbour

Now just 3km² of saltmarsh, mudflats and tidal creeks, Pagham Harbour represents the broad eastern end of what was once a tidal channel 6km long and 0.5-1km wide separating the island of Selsey from the mainland (Figure 4). In AD 681 Bede described a narrow isthmus joining the island to the mainland on the western side, although the Roman road running south from Chichester to the villa at Sidlesham seems to have crossed to Selsey at SZ 856962, where the B2145 still skirts the head of the westernmost creek of the harbour; possibly the isthmus was at this point, immediately west of the island's northern tip. On the other hand a very accurate map of 1778 shows the Ferry Channel, Pagham Harbour's western branch, extending as a wide tapering estuary a good kilometre to the south-west of the B2145, an expanse of tidal water that had all been reclaimed by 1813; this suggests that the isthmus was further round, at about SZ 850950, conforming more closely with Bede's description.

The nature of the isthmus is also unclear. It may have been a low brickearth watershed, a piece of the coastal plain that by chance remained above water when the stream valleys to east and west were flooded by the rising sea. Alternatively, and more likely, given the way in which the channel evolved later on, with the Broad Rife crossing the site, it may have been a shingle bar or **tombolo,** traces of which have subsequently been either removed or concealed under later deposits. Wave fronts passing round the headland would have been progressively refracted (bent), creating a sheltered low energy environment halfway round the tidal channel, an area in which deposition of this type was likely to occur. Once a bar or tombolo was formed, sedimentation on either side of it would have been progressive, explaining the decline and eventual disappearance of the medieval 'new town' of Wardur (at SZ 8697). In 1588 ships of 40 tons could still reach Wardur's quay, but continuing silting meant that by 1852 only 25-ton ships could navigate the winding, shrinking creeks and then only once or twice a week. Kip's 1610 map shows that by then the south-western creek had completely silted up to create the **floodplain** of the Broad Rife in very much its present form.

The natural silting of Pagham Harbour displays a classic feedback mechanism. As sediment filled the heads of the creeks and coated the upper surfaces of the tidal mudflats, the volume of the tidal compartment was reduced: this meant less sea water was entering and leaving the Harbour on each tide to clear the sediment. Saltmarsh vegetation also colonized the higher areas of the mudflats, the plant stems and root systems creating further sediment traps and accelerating the silting process.

An additional factor has been the development of a bar or two spits at the Harbour entrance. An Armada map of 1588 shows two opposed spits as at present, but many changes have occurred between then and now. The southern spit has tended to grow as a result of the onshore movement of sediment and its redistribution by longshore drift. By 1672 the southern spit was 1000m long and growing at the expense of the northern, which was 700m long. By 1774 the southern spit was 1200m long, by 1823 1400m, by 1843 1650m and by 1874 it was over 2000m long and diverting the entrance channel northwards so that it eroded low clay cliffs to within 250m of Pagham church. It was to stop this erosion that the Harbour was sealed off in 1876, leaving a section of the entrance channel as a lake, Pagham Lagoon. Behind the now-continuous shingle barrier many of the saltings were successfully converted to pasture. Reclamation progressed until 1910, when seas driven by south-easterly gales broke through the centre of the bar, turning it once more into two opposed spits. The implication is that the original, sixteenth century, spits also represent the broken remnants of a baymouth bar that was storm breached in an earlier cycle of bar development, although no map evidence of this survives; possibly there were several cycles of bar building and breaching, as are known elsewhere: the shingle barrier at the mouth of Christchurch Harbour in Dorset went through as many as five cycles of accretion and breaching in the 100 years leading up to 1938.

Twentieth-century changes have been slightly erratic, with an initial southward shift in the position of the entrance channel (indicating reversed longshore drift) until, by 1944, it was almost opposite Church Norton, the reverse of the 1874 situation. In 1955 storm waves created two breaches in the barrier: the isolated section between the breaches was rolled forwards and spread some 800m into the Harbour, leaving a very wide entrance gap. After 1959 the southern spit grew steadily northwards again, narrowing the entrance: in one year its tip advanced as much as 75m. The entrance at high water is now roughly where it was in 1910 and 1672, its position fixed by training groynes. Between high and low water marks, however, the northward drift has continued, taking the low water entrance 800m east-north-east of the high water entrance.

The shingle for these spits and bars is derived partly from the erosion of the raised beach sediment between Selsey Bill and Church Norton, transferred north-eastwards and organized by longshore drift, and partly from the onshore movement of seabed sediment in The Park, the old open-water anchorage to the south-east of the barrier. Behind the barrier the saltmarsh continues to develop and consolidate with the tidal compartment increasingly confined to three principal creeks, White's Creek, Mill Channel and Ferry Channel: these surround a central area, almost 1km^2 of saltmarsh, which may eventually become an island.

THE BLACK ROCK RAISED BEACH AND FOSSIL CLIFF

© Crown Copyright

The Black Rock raised beach, a focus of geomorphological interest since it was first described by Gideon Mantell in the 1820s, is exposed in the modern cliff face at Brighton Marina (TQ 336033). An extension of the beach as far east as Roedean School was destroyed by marine erosion in the nineteenth century. The cliff between the Palace Pier and Black Rock has been encased in concrete since the 1820s, but that from Black Rock to Rottingdean was left undefended until the **undercliff** walk was built against the **notch** in the 1930s. The 150-200m stepback of the unprotected cliff is very evident at the Marina, and it represents a mean erosion rate of about 1.5m per year.

The raised beach is composed of rounded flint gravel with a little sand and it rests on a shore platform terminating eastwards at the foot of a fossil cliff (Figure 5). The beach sediments are overlaid by angular chalk rubble, the result of subaerial degradation of the cliff, probably under the cold conditions associated with the fall in sea level that stranded the beach. To the west, during the excavation work for the Marina, a layer of windblown sand was seen to rest directly on the beach material. The beach has so far yielded only one human artefact, a water-rolled Acheulian (palaeolithic) hand axe. The lower part of the fossil cliff is vertical, whilst the upper part is bevelled at 45°. Presumably the upper segment was exposed to weathering for longer and thus became degraded before it too was buried. The slope-over-wall form is very common on the hard-rock coasts of Dorset, Devon and Cornwall, where it probably also represents a survival from earlier warm and cold episodes.

The chalk rubble is replaced westwards and upwards by finer, stratified

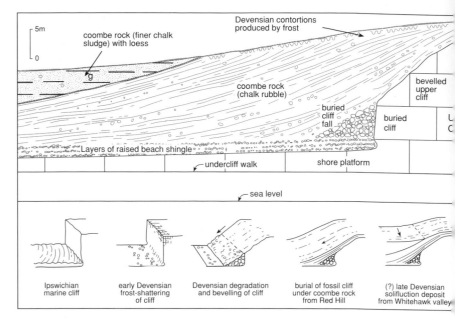

Figure 5: The Black Rock raised beach: a natural section

coombe rock, here a chalky sediment with flints and occasional sarsen boulders. Sarsens, which are uncommon in Sussex, are eroded remnants of a thin layer of Palaeogene sandstone which is thought to have overlaid the Chalk. The stratification of the periglacial deposit implies that it was laid down a series of muddy flows, first from Red Hill and then from the Sheepcote and Whitehawk valleys (now dry). It is assumed that this activity occurred during brief summer thaws. The yellowish colour of the stratified deposit suggests an admixture of loess (windblown silt), again typical of tundra landscapes such as southern Britain during cold climatic conditions. These deposits contain the remains of mammoth, horse and woolly rhinoceros.

The Black Rock raised beach is one of several in Britain indicating a mean sea level about 7m above that of the present day. The top of the Black Rock beach rises to 11.9m. It has not so far been positively dated. The few molluscs contained in the sediment are similar to those of modern British beaches and prove temperate conditions. This is to be expected since relatively high sea levels tend to be associated with warm, interglacial stages when the volume of water locked up in glacial ice is minimal. There is some evidence to indicate that the beach is Ipswichian in age: (1) beaches at similar altitudes throughout the world have been dated to the Ipswichian (OI Stage 5e, Table 2, page 12), about 125 000 years ago; and (2) the Black Rock raised beach apparently extends westwards to Selsey where, as we have seen, it overlies pollen-bearing silts which have been interpreted as Ipswichian.

Present sea level might have been the same as the Ipswichian but for plate tectonics: the very slight enlargement of the ocean basins may mean that, although Flandrian sea level has recovered post-glacially, it is 7-8m below the Ipswichian level. This mechanism may explain the apparent down-stepping of the sea levels in successive interglacials.

Raised beaches in southern Britain are found at a range of altitudes implying, to some geomorphologists, several distinct periods of formation. The 30-37m raised beach at Goodwood, Slindon and Boxgrove, for example, is now thought to be of Cromerian age (OI Stage 13, Table 2). Recent work has shown that a small lake existed in front of the fossil Cromerian cliff at Boxgrove and that palaeolithic people frequented the site, leaving their flint tools round its shores; they lived on a level land surface at 40m OD that was built of Slindon Sand and Slindon Silt deposits resting on top of the fossil Cromerian beach. Streams flowing 250m further south were cutting channels into the sand. Boxgrove man, tentatively classified as *Homo cf heidelbergensis,* hunted red deer, giant deer, horse, rhinoceros and bear. Interglacial conditions evidently existed at that time, although the sea had retreated at least 300m south from the old cliffline, which stood about 70m north of the findspot of a human shinbone. The discrepancy between the coastline and the cliffline could be explained in terms of a falling sea level towards the close of the Cromerian warm stage.

The extension of the Black Rock beach westwards from Brighton reaches heights of 14m, an altitude above that currently associated with worldwide Ipswichian sea levels. It has been suggested that at a late stage in the Ipswichian sea level rose dramatically, though briefly, due to an Antarctic ice-surge. In the Ipswichian, as today, parts of the Antarctic ice sheet were afloat, forming ice shelves. Large areas of shelf-ice may have broken off, floating away as enormous tabular icebergs; when these eventually drifted into lower latitudes and melted, they would have caused sea levels to rise worldwide. The evidence supporting the hypothesis is limited, but the raised beach sediments of the West Sussex coastal plain are consistent with it. An alternative explanation is that the Black Rock raised beach may represent two distinct phases of beach formation only a few metres apart vertically but occurring in different interglacials. The Portland raised beach is now thought to be twofold, the slightly higher western beach dating from 210 000 BP (OI Stage 7 see Table 2), the eastern from 125 000 BP. Similar findings have come from the Gower Peninsula, where beach remnants dating from 210 000 and 125 000 BP have been discovered very close together only a few metres above the modern beach. A similar elision of sea levels is seen on the South Devon coast, where the modern shore platform slopes almost imperceptibly into one formed when sea level was 4m higher. Nevertheless, little reliance can be placed on long-distance correlations by height alone; the central English Channel, including the Isle of Wight, may have uplifted by 40m or more as the result of earth movement during the Middle and Late Pleistocene, so it is likely that height correlations even between East and West Sussex may be suspect.

The Black Rock beach contains erratic material such as granite, slate and porphyry. The same controversy surrounds these erratics as that prompted by the Selsey erratics discussed in the previous section. It might be added here that the arrival of the erratics need not be associated with the high interglacial sea we have just been discussing since they may have been exhumed from still older sediments. The Goodwood raised beach in West Sussex, for example, contains erratic material and may therefore be the source of the erratics incorporated in the lower beach. Erratics have been found on the foreshore at Rottingdean and Saltdean, probably eroded out of the Black Rock beach and representing the latest recycling of the material.

It is possible that, as at Selsey, the shore platform at Black Rock may be older than the beach sediment. Some corroboration comes from Portland in Dorset, where the eastern raised beach of Ipswichian age shows evidence of a cold phase between platform cutting and beach deposition. The fact that the upper, north-western part of the Portland platform is still covered by beach sediment from a pre-Ipswichian interglacial seems to confirm that the whole platform may have been eroded in the earlier interglacial, with some of the beach material being replaced or reworked in the Ipswichian. Both upper (Goodwood-Boxgrove) and lower (Selsey-Black Rock) raised beaches should be regarded as composite, each beach resulting from complex erosion and deposition phases in more than one interglacial.

Access

Pedestrian ramps lead down from the southern end of Arundel Street to the undercliff walk: this provides direct access to the beach, which is visible immediately east of the ramp complex. There is a large supermarket car park at the Marina, offering a good overall view of the beach.

THE MOUTH OF THE RIVER OUSE

The coastal cliffs at Castle Hill, Newhaven (Photo 1 and Figure 6), illustrate well how the shape of a landform and the processes by which it evolves are controlled by rock-type and time.

The lower two-thirds of the cliffs are made of hard, pure (98% CaCO₃) Upper Chalk. No dip is visible because the bedding planes dip slightly to the north, into the cliff.

The Chalk is undercut at the high water mark and blocks loosened along joints and bedding planes (the networks of cracks inherent in the rock) drop to the foreshore: the result is clean, near vertical cliff in homogeneous white Chalk. On top, and preserved in a shallow downfold, the Newhaven **Syncline**, is a rare outcrop of Palaeogene sands and clays, which are both softer and vertically more variable that the Chalk. Because they are weaker and retain rainwater, these beds may from time to time move suddenly. The slope may fail in a slide (the rock slipping over a water-lubricated surface without changing its shape significantly) or

Photo 1: Cliffs at Castle Hill, Newhaven
The cliff in the distance is undergoing active erosion by the sea. The degraded cliff in the foreground is protected from active marine erosion by the accumulation of shingle on the western side of the breakwater. Photo: Rodney Castleden.

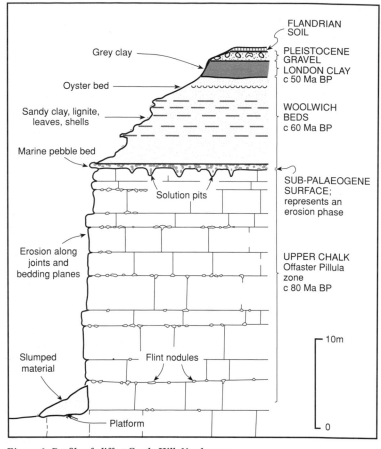

Figure 6: Profile of cliff at Castle Hill, Newhaven

The shape of the cliff is closely related to its geology. This is the only natural exposure of the basal bed of the Sussex Palaeogene, the 'Reading Bottom Bed', made of cemented green-coated flint pebbles. The solution pits in the Chalk were made by acidified groundwater passing through the overlying Woolwich Beds

a flow (the beds moving by continuous deformation in a semi-liquid or plastic state). This has produced a gently inclined but hummocky slope facet along the cliff top (often at 10-20°) as well as an apron of slipped debris along the cliff foot.

Acidified water passing through the Palaeogene beds has dissolved the Chalk in places to form conical solution pits in the unconformity that separates the Palaeogene from the Chalk. This is one of the few places where the unconformity may be seen; it represents a phase of erosion lasting perhaps 25 million years during which the Chalk was raised over 200m and the top 50m were removed by erosion. There are several solution pipes 1-2m in diameter and two larger ones 8m in diameter (TQ 444999, 445999). The eastern one, cut in half by cliff retreat, has turned into a debris chute, a route by which sand and clay are delivered to the undercliff: the clayey lining of the solution pit contains a range of aluminium minerals, including the only known occurrence in Britain of Nordstrandite $Al(OH)_3$.

In its natural state the cliff foot is washed by the sea at high water, so that the slumped, incoherent Palaeogene debris is quickly dispersed and the vertical Chalk Hill, e.g. at TQ 438999, where the sea is at work undercutting the Chalk cliff and extending the shore platform is a 1° ramp mainly by the abrading effect of flint pebbles rolling back and forth across the bare rock surface. It is uncovered at low water.

Further east, at Castle Hill and the Fort, the situation is very different. The long breakwater impedes the natural eastward movement of beach material by longshore drift (Figure 7): a large accumulation of shingle covers the shore platform and prevents waves from reaching the cliff foot. As a result, occasional falls of chalk and the more prolific slides and flows of Palaeogene material have built up a chaotic undercliff which obscures the lower half of the Chalk cliff. Since the Chalk cliff is no longer being undercut, its position has stabilised: the foot of the Palaeogene facet is also more or less stationary. Once the Palaeogene beds have reached a stable angle of rest, the mass movement will virtually come to a halt. The large area covered by vegetation, both on the Palaeogene cliff slope and on the undercliff, implies that the abandoned and degraded cliffline is already close to stability.

The speed with which the cliffs have generated a substantial undercliff and become degraded can be gauged from the dates of the harbour works. The 800m-long breakwater was built in 1890, replacing a 150m stone groyne erected in 1830: both were designed to prevent the mouth of the Ouse from being closed by drifting shingle.

The river mouth itself is modern and artificial: cut in 1537, recut in 1644, it was repeatedly blocked by longshore drift. The natural, pre-1537

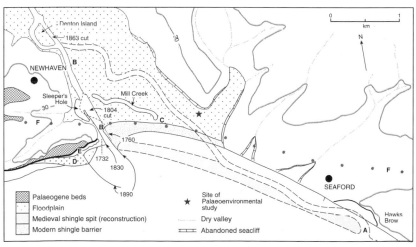

Figure 7: Changes in the mouth of the River Ouse
A, outfall until 1530; B, new course cut 1530 and recut 1743; C, outfall cut 1650;
D, shingle accumulated since 1890; E, slumped Palaeogene debris; F, axis of
Newhaven Syncline. Other dates are the building dates of successive piers designed
to keep the present outfall open

course of the Ouse was due south-east from the swing bridge to the Buckle. The mouth was fixed at the eastern extremity of the floodplain by the outgrowth of the shingle bank from Castle Hill. Like the Adur, it is a classic example of river mouth deflection by longshore drift. The early medieval outfall was even further to the south-east, at Seaford. A fragment of the medieval north-eastern floodplain edge has escaped destruction by marine erosion – the low-lying area to the north and east of the Martello Tower. The shingle beach between Castle Hill and the Martello Tower was at least 200m to seaward, enabling the Ouse to thread its way along the site of the modern beach and reach the sea immediately west of Hawks Brow.

'The same harbour is so narrow an entrance that scarcely two vessels can enter it side by side. On each side, two headlands raised heavenwards slope down with a gradual hill by which every wave is broken when strong winds arise. There, neither anchor holds the ships, nor rope checks them, but they do not at all fear either the east, nor the north, nor the north-west-by-west winds.'

This description of 'Sefordt' in 1058 by the monk Balgerus well describes the last meander of the Ouse which we may assume lay east of where the Martello Tower now stands. Seaford declined as a port partly for historical reasons (frequent French raids, depopulation by the Black Death, shortage of timber) and partly for geomorphological reasons (flooding and continual blocking by drifting shingle). Seaford was abandoned and a 'new haven' was created under Castle Hill: by 1580 the old port was described as 'a duckpool'.

The beach between TQ 447000 and 463000 is sheltered from south-west winds by the Newhaven breakwater, so that it experiences south-easterlies as its dominant winds. This short stretch of coastline therefore has a westward longshore drift, which explains why its beaches thicken and broaden towards the west. Between the Buckle and the Martello Tower (TQ 468997 and 484984) the eastward longshore drift resumes, leaving a long stretch of beach suffering from progressive beach starvation. Beach nourishment, the artificial addition of beach shingle, has proved temporarily satisfactory.

The floor of the 1km wide floodplain which separates the old and new river mouths assumed its present form in the Devensian cold stage (Figure 8). At that time much of the ocean water was imprisoned in ice sheets, sea level was up to 100m lower than now, and the braided channels of a periglacial river criss-crossed the rock floor – in some places scoring it with multiple channel forms, in others planing it smooth with continually migrating channels. That rock floor is now at −12m OD at Lewes, descending to −30m at the river mouth. The lowest levels were probably eroded during one of the Devensian stadials or ice-maxima, in either 28 000 or 18 000 bp. The Thames, in its present estuary, was eroding down to −40m and −30m OD during these events and it is likely that the Sussex rivers were behaving similarly. The long profile of the Devensian rock floor steepens towards the sea. This has been interpreted as **rejuvenation** stimulated by the lowering of sea level to around −100m,

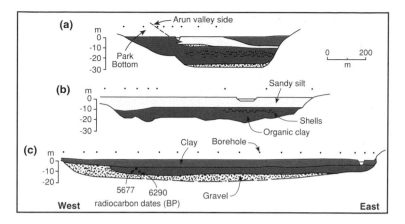

Figure 8: Sections through Sussex floodplains

(a) River Arun at Arundel; (b) River Adur 2km south of Bramber; (c),River Ouse 1km south of Lewes. The gravel is assumed to be a Devensian river deposit

but this seems unlikely, as the 100m coastline was 350km away by crow-flight, near The Lizard: too far to exert any control. The withdrawal of the sea simply enabled further erosion, both downward and seaward from the present river mouths, to take place. There is a tendency for the profile to be steeper on Hastings Beds and Chalk, gentler on Greensand and Gault and Weald Clays. The steepening between Lewes and Newhaven may thus be lithologically controlled.

In the Devensian, the valley sides were trimmed back to within a few metres of their present positions, while the Ouse continued, probably south from Seaford, across a subdued plain to join the Channel River, whose northern palaeovalley lay only 14km south of the present mouth of the Ouse (Figure 9). This northern palaeovalley, a broad shallow trough bounded by low but well-marked bluffs, is a typical periglacial river valley eroded by the multiple channels of a braided river carrying large volumes of sand and gravel: it received as right-bank tributaries the lengthened Cuckmere, Ouse, Adur and Arun. There are even submerged minor valleys heading up towards Worthing (the Findon valley) and Brighton (the Steine), implying that these major Chalk dry valleys also once guided rivers towards the northern palaeovalley. In the 4-6km immediately south of the present coastline all trace of the submerged valleys seems to have gone, presumably because the interfluves have been removed by Flandrian wave action: there is therefore an element of speculation in reconstructing those segments of the Devensian rivers.

In deeper water, the seabed on each side of the submerged valleys is extremely flat, as if the interfluves had been sawn off. In fact the entire Channel floor has very little relief. It represents a Pleistocene unconformity cutting across many geological structures. One view (Curry 1989) is that this erosion is taking place now on the seabed. It would seem more likely that shoreline processes are responsible, and that different areas of the seabed are subjected to erosion by these processes at different

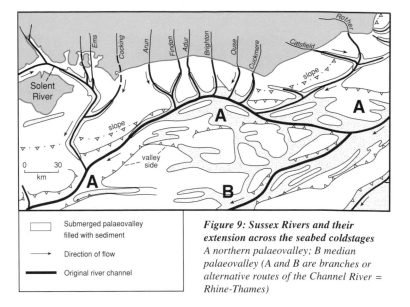

Submerged palaeovalley filled with sediment

→ Direction of flow

Original river channel

Figure 9: Sussex Rivers and their extension across the seabed coldstages
A northern palaeovalley; B median palaeovalley (A and B are branches or alternative routes of the Channel River = Rhine-Thames)

times, according to sea level. As the sea rose from its lowest level, every square centimetre of the central and eastern Channel floor will have been subjected to wave action.

The onset of interglacial (i.e. present-day) conditions brought sea level rapidly up from –100m at 14 000 bp to –20m at 8000 bp, then more slowly to –2m by 2000 bp. The Ouse, like other south coast valleys, was invaded by the sea to form a deep water inlet with moderately steep sides, which penetrated inland to Lewes. Sea waves lapping the shores of the estuary retouched the Devensian river cliffs, adding some low sea cliffs. The slopes of the valley sides are thus polygenetic, although it seems unlikely that trimming by meander migration (the standard explanation for such forms) has played a significant part. There is very little evidence that meanders of lowland 'clay' rivers migrate on a significant scale, or that the Flandrian Ouse would be capable of eroding cliffs.

The open estuary lasted approximately from 5000 to 1300 bp, during which time it gradually became shallower, filling with a complex sequence of interbedded river, beach and estuarine deposits. The sheltered conditions necessary for silting were enhanced by the growth of the shingle spit across the estuary mouth, but this development, probably beginning with a short spit early in the estuary's history, was not completed until the medieval period.

Palaeoenvironmental studies of a fossil beach at the foot of the degraded sea-cliff at Bishopstone (TQ 465002) show that the site was open to fully marine conditions around 500-100 BC – surprisingly late. The shingle spit or bar must have been built across the estuary entrance fairly rapidly after that, because by the seventh century AD the Bishopstone beach had been buried under silty clays containing *Scrobicularia*, indicating that by then it was a low-energy muddy saltmarsh. The Ouse and probably the other Sussex estuaries remained open to the sea until rather late; the high tidal range may have helped to keep their entrances open, but once human land reclamation began to reduce their tidal compartments closure was rapid. There is no difficulty in supposing that the Ouse shingle spit grew rapidly. The spit blocking the Adur mouth grew 5.6km in the 200 years following 1587, a rate of 28m per year; the Ouse spit, developing in a very similar situation, was only 4km long altogether.

The long gap (4km) in the cliffline between Castle Hill and Seaford Head has traditionally been explained in terms of marine erosion exploiting a structural weakness in the Chalk, the axis of the Newhaven Syncline, but compression of the rock in synclines usually increases its resistance, as at Mount Caburn near Lewes. More significant is the north-west to south-east trend of the floodplain's morphological axis at Newhaven, which originally continued to Seaford and then apparently turned south-west. The floodplain has been intercepted by a modern coastline trending west-north-west to east-south-east. It is the low angle of interception which explains the wide gate in the cliffs. The low Chalk bluffs between TQ 468997 and 480988 are really remnants of the north-eastern side of the Ouse valley.

Access

Castle Hill cliff foot is accessible from a waterfront car park at TQ 450000; from there, the degraded cliffline is clearly visible, and an easy walk westwards along the backshore leads to the natural cliffline. The cliff top is accessible by an unmade road up to the coastguard station from TQ 447005: this is best tackled on foot. On the cliff top, the scars of several old landslips can be inspected with safety.

Bishopstone Beach is accessible from the Buckle car park (TQ 468997). For the medieval outfall of the Ouse at Seaford there is seafront parking east of the Martello Tower (TQ 484985).

SEAFORD HEAD AND HOPE GAP

The precipitous cliffs at Seaford Head rising to 85m are developed in Upper Chalk; since they are further to the south of the axis of the Newhaven Syncline than the Castle Hill cliffs, they throw out a lower fossil zone, *Micraster coranguinum*. The straight cliffline running 1.7km east-south-east from Seaford Head follows the strike and is thus reinforced and controlled by a major set of vertical joints.

On the golf course at TQ 495984 are deposits of orange-brown sands, silts and clays. These are often held to be remnants of the same Palaeogene beds visible at Newhaven, but, although they are almost certainly derived from Palaeogene beds preserved in the syncline, they seem to have been loosened by frost-churning, transported by solifluction, wind, sheetwash and possibly periglacial streams, and re-deposited at lower levels. Their stratigraphy is significantly different from that of the Castle Hill beds: the junction with the Chalk, for example, appears to be more recent with no trace of consolidation. They are probably Palaeogene beds modified during the Pleistocene. A fine natural section through these ambiguous deposits can be seen at Short Cliff, where they rest on a sub-horizontal bench apparently eroded by the River Cuckmere during a pre-Devensian cold stage.

Some new fossil evidence released by cliff retreat is emerging and this may help to clarify the origin of the deposits. A mass of Short Cliff Beds dropped to the foreshore in 1992 close to Hope Gap and from its upper layers came the left metatarsal of a horse and a section of mammoth tusk. A further section of tusk was found in March 1994 at the same spot. So far no associated mammoth bones have been found. The tusk was in remarkably good condition; although fractured in several places during the cliff-fall, it had suffered no damage in antiquity: there were no signs of abrasion due to water-rolling. The circumstances imply that the tusk was not washed into place by the River Cuckmere but collected from a kill-site, carried to the Hope Gap site and either deposited on the open sandy surface and deliberately left there or accidentally lost. Finds of stone tools suggest that there may have been a human settlement in the Hope Valley just 300m to the south-west and this would be consistent with finds of animal debris in the vicinity. The horse came from an extinct species, *Equus ferus,* which flourished in Sussex 200 000 - 13 000 years ago in a dry cold steppe environment. The size of the mammoth tusk suggests that it too belongs to a cold phase prior to the Devensian; thus, limited though it is, the fossil evidence points to an origin for what we may call the Short Cliff Beds in the Wolstonian cold stage, 200 000 - 130 000 BP.

Photo 2: Solution pipes at Short Cliff
The vertical sectioning of these pipes has been produced by cliff retreat. The jointing of the Chalk shows well in the notch at the foot of the picture. Photo: Rodney Castleden.

Water percolating through the Short Cliff Beds has been acidified so that the underlying Chalk has been subjected to aggressive solution, forming pipes. These pipes show up well in the cliff face at Seaford Head as funnel-shaped pits extending up to 5m down the cliff top; although the highest cliffs have been stripped of Short Cliff Beds, remnants let down into pipes survive. At Short Cliff, sections are visible through deeper pipes which descend all the way to high water mark as chimneys which are circular in cross-section: some still contain sediment, others have been flushed out (see Photo 2).

Out on the Chalk shore platform, 19 circular holes about 1m in diameter penetrating the platform show that piping descends well below present high water mark. Several have a circular rim of solid chalk which has been hardened by a limestone precipitate, re-deposited like stalactite in a limestone cave by water passing down the pipe at the time of its formation. These platform pipes may have the appearance of severely weathered stone-built wellheads, but they are entirely natural (Figure 10 and Photo 3).

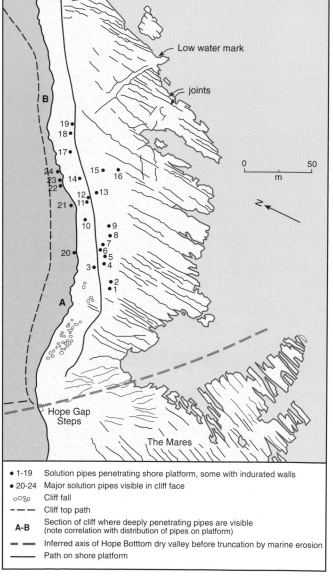

Figure 10: Detailed features of the shore platform at Hope Gap and Short Cliff

The shore platform is well-developed here. South of Hope Gap it forms a promontory called The Mares at low water. Waves roll pebbles along joints which are roughly normal to the beach, eroding gutters which are often slightly sinuous in form and up to 1m deep. They function as drainage channels for the platform as the tide ebbs.

On the eastern side of Seaford Head, two small dry valleys converge on Hope Gap, a hanging valley perched 14m above high water mark. Controversy surrounds the origin of Chalk dry valleys. Disagreement among geomorphologists is mainly due to the existence of several different types of valley formed by different processes. The major dry valleys were desiccated long enough ago to have been beheaded by the retreating escarpment. They were master streams in the Pliocene and early Pleistocene, flowing from the interior of the Weald across the Chalk downs in temperate and cold stages alike under high water table conditions, and continuing in the cold stages out to join the Channel River. Complex sequences of sediment in some of the valley floors show that they were modified in several successive cold stages. The gradual incision of the river valleys lowered the water table in the South Downs, starving some streams, while river capture in the clay lands to the north ensured the success of others. The Cuckmere, for example, is a survivor of this competition, while the Jevington valley (TQ 5601 to 5299) is a casualty. The permafrost conditions of the later Pleistocene cold stages nevertheless ensured at least seasonal river flows in the South Downs

Photo 3: A well head at Short Cliff
This is a solution pipe penetrating an unknown distance below high water mark and may have been formed at a time of lower sea level. It has been sectioned horizontally by the extension of the modern shore platform. Photo: Rodney Castleden.

when the snows melted in summer. The hundreds of minor dry valleys of the Chalk back slope and **scarp slope** originated in this way, to be desiccated at the onset of temperate, interglacial conditions. Nearly all the valleys in this second group have formed with the escarpment in its present position, which explains why so many valleys head immediately behind or immediately in front of the scarp crest. Hope Bottom and Cliff Bottom belong to the second group and will have been inactive for 10 000 years: it is certain that none of the Chalk dry valleys was formed postglacially.

Hope Gap steps pass in front of a decaying section through the valley fill. This brown sandy silt rests on unsound Chalk, which is *in situ* Chalk disrupted by the many periglacial freeze-thaw cycles of Pleistocene cold stages. The re-entrant in the shore platform to the south-east shows where the former course of Hope Bottom continued to join the Cuckmere valley. Disrupted Chalk under the valley's axis has been eroded easily by wave action.

Access

Seaford Head cliff top can be reached on foot in two ways: along the coast path from the Seaford seafront car park (TQ 488982), or along the metalled track west-south-west from the summit of South Hill, where there is informal parking space. The road up to South Hill follows the stripped structural surface of the Newhaven Syncline.

Hope Gap is reached by the path south-east from South Hill, forking right after 350m into Hope Bottom. At Hope Gap there are concrete steps to the beach. Here, at low tide, there is access to the shore platform (The Mares), the cliff face of Seaford Head, and a way along the platform below Short Cliff to regain the cliff top at the coastguard cottages.

Safety

It is advisable to consult a tide table when planning a walk on the shore platform. The safest time to attempt this kind of walk is during the ebb, when the tide is about two-thirds out and falling. The cautious visitor will stay on the cliff top when the tide is rising: incoming tides can cover the shore platform alarmingly quickly. When walking on the cliff top, it is important to keep well back from the cliff edge – no closer than about 3m. However solid the cliff edge may appear, it can give way suddenly, without warning. It also follows that there is some danger from falling rocks at the cliff foot, so it is sensible to keep at least 8m in front of a high cliff.

CUCKMERE HAVEN

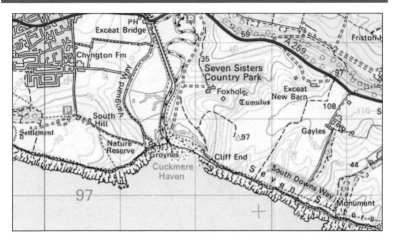

The lower reach of the Cuckmere valley is best known for its unusually well-developed river meanders. In addition it has valley meanders, a rare marine delta and a floodplain flooring which is arguably the most beautiful water gap through the South Downs. These features are fully accessible and also visible from some superb vantage points.

As it approaches the sea, the Cuckmere meanders across a 0.75km wide floodplain bounded by valley sides which rise abruptly and often steeply to about 60m. The trough-shaped valley originated in a similar way to the Ouse, Adur and Arun valleys. The (Devensian?) bedrock floor stands at −13.1m close to the floodplain edge at Exceat Bridge and, although unproved, it is likely that a scalloped, nearly flat rock floor declines to about −20m beneath the modern river mouth. The valley walls are sub-parallel and display valley meanders with a mean wavelength of 1.3km. Large wavelength may be produced by rivers with either high peak discharges or a coarse load: both would be applicable to the Cuckmere in Pleistocene cold stages.

As sea level rose at the onset of the present temperate stage, the valley was flooded as far upstream as Alfriston to form a ria. Some marine trimming occurred, although, as in the Ouse valley, it is hard to distinguish between steep valley side slopes formed by the sea and those formed by lateral river erosion in the Devensian. Even so, the freshness of the low (5m) cliffs along the east side of the valley south of Exceat Barn suggests recent formation by marine trimming; the identification of iron age beach deposits at the foot of very similar low cliffs at

Bishopstone in the Ouse valley would certainly seem to support this. The major cliffing in the water gaps of the South Downs is clearly the result of undercutting by a high-energy agent of erosion. It is evident, for instance, that Hindover Hill (TQ 510010), with its drop of 92m and 40° slope, has been formed as a river cliff by a dynamic laterally eroding, probably periglacial river: facing inland in a sheltered inlet, it could not be a sea-cliff. The lower slopes of the valley sides are thus polygenetic.

The thick cover of alluvium carpeting the Cuckmere floodplain was deposited initially under estuarine conditions below Alfriston, and during river floods upstream. The changeover to deposition of silt, clay and peat was partly due to a change in climate. The basal layers have been radiocarbon dated to the very beginning of the Flandrian, 9400 bp, at Arlington (TQ 538074). Interestingly, sea level was still low at that time, about –40m OD, which reinforces the argument that distant changes in sea level do not have a decisive control over a river's tendency to aggrade or incise. The accumulation of sediment in the Sussex rias was also assisted by human activity. Six thousand years ago, the clay soils of the Wealden catchment areas were protected by a thick forest. Since then, the soil has been exposed by piecemeal clearance for charcoal, building materials, firewood and timber for shipbuilding; large areas have come under the plough: the loosened soil is washed into ditches and streams to be re-deposited on floodplains. Much of the upper layer of alluvium is thus indirectly anthropogenic in origin.

As the open ria became silted up, it shallowed and narrowed to a meandering estuary with flanking tidal mud flats. On these Flandrian deposits, the Cuckmere has developed some of the finest river meanders to be seen anywhere, especially the 'hairpin' meander at Exceat Barn. One modern view is that rivers meander as a means of adjusting their gradient: the more tortuous the river channel, the gentler its gradient becomes. Low gradients are often associated with a fine sediment load: clearly small particles can be transported at very low velocities, and these in turn are achieved by reducing the gradient. It is also thought that the extra work involved in flowing through a lengthened channel, especially near the river mouth, may be a way of balancing the river's energy budget. Between Alfriston and the sea, the Cuckmere's natural channel has a sinuosity (channel distance divided by crow flight distance) of 1.84, increasing to 2.00 below Exceat Bridge. The valley meanders, associated with the sand and gravel load available in the Devensian periglacial stage, have a sinuosity of only 1.1 and thus maintain the steeper gradient appropriate to the coarse load.

The spectacular channel meanders were bypassed in 1846 to reduce flooding. The present mouth of the river is artificial too. Like the Ouse, the Cuckmere was repeatedly deflected eastwards by a shingle spit and from time to time had its natural outfall forced to the extreme eastern edge of the floodplain, directly below Cliff End (Figure 11). Becoming blocked with shingle, it created a new mouth by breaking through the bar further west; the latest of these westerly mouths has been fixed by training groynes.

The shingle spit probably began to develop as soon as the ria was

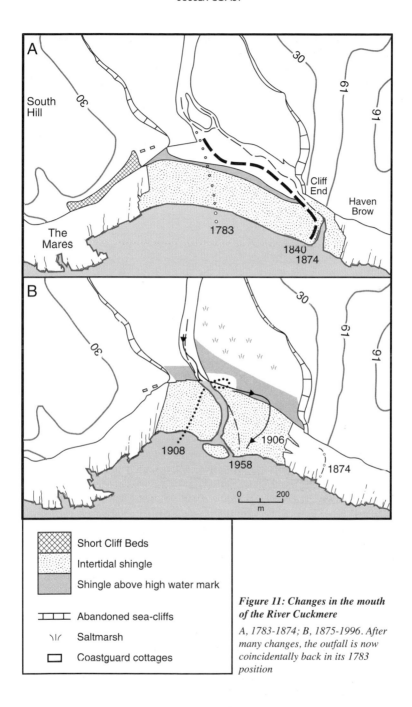

Figure 11: Changes in the mouth
of the River Cuckmere

A, 1783-1874; B, 1875-1996. After
many changes, the outfall is now
coincidentally back in its 1783
position

formed. Its extension across the Haven was initially hindered by strong
tidal currents going in and out of the large inlet. Nevertheless, the spit
helped to provide sheltered conditions in which estuarine silting could

occur. As the ria silted up the tidal compartment contracted and the spit rapidly extended across to Cliff End.

In terms of catchment area and discharge, the Cuckmere is the smallest of the four 'Downland' rivers in Sussex, only one-quarter the size of the Ouse; its feeders are, moreover, threatened with dismemberment by river capture. To ensure that this relatively feeble river can keep its present outfall open, it has been closely confined between two training groynes; at their seaward end, the river diverges and drops its load among several continually altering distributaries, forming a small delta.

Cuckmere Haven is thus a focus of deposition. As with other inlets of the Sussex coast, wave refraction produces a low-energy environment in which sedimentation can occur. Wave refraction is a very common phenomenon; wave fronts move at different speeds depending on water depth and so wrap themselves round the coastline, spreading out in bays so that the wave energy is dissipated over a greater length of shoreline. Conversely, wave fronts converge on headlands so that wave energy is concentrated on a shorter length of shoreline. Because of this, headlands experience erosion as their dominant process, whereas bays and inlets experience mainly deposition.

Access

Cuckmere Haven (western side) can be reached from South Hill direct, or via Hope Gap, or by the footpath running south from the Exceat Bridge car park (TQ 513993). There is no bridge across the mouth of the Cuckmere, so the eastern side can only be reached by footpath from the car park at Exceat Barn (TQ 518995).

THE SEVEN SISTERS AND BEACHY HEAD

The Seven Sisters

The impressive Chalk cliffs between Cuckmere Haven and Eastbourne are among the most famous in the country. They include the Seven Sisters (see Photo 4), Birling Gap and the headlands of Beltout and Beachy Head. The Chalk here is homogeneous and relatively unresistant, producing straight, clean, near-vertical cliffs, but no caves, arches or stacks.

The Seven Sisters are straight in plan, developed at right angles to the dip and, in these respects, somewhat similar to Seaford Head. Where the cliffline is different and distinguished from all others is in its profile (Figure 12). Its distinctive switchback crest with seven rounded summits has made it an unmistakable landmark for generations of sailors.

Photo 4: The Seven Sisters from Hope Gap

The shore platform of The Mares is clearly visible in the foreground, Short Cliff to the left. The cliff fall that yielded the horse and mammoth remains is seen top left; the photograph was taken before their discovery. Photo: Rodney Castleden.

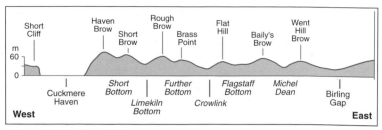

Figure 12: The Seven Sisters

The Chalk dry valleys left hanging by marine erosion are shown in italics. The vertical scale is four times the horizontal scale

The shape of the crest is a relic of a fossil subaerial landscape, i.e. it was formed by 'dry-land' processes. A series of short dry valleys draining the Chalk backslope has been truncated by marine erosion to form the low points in the crest. When the rising sea first drowned this landscape, the coastline would have been indented and roughly parallel with the contours behind the cliff top. Wave refraction and the jointing of the Chalk have combined to produce a classic straightened coastline. The longest of the hanging dry valleys, Gap Bottom, is 1.8km long: the shortest, Short Bottom, is only 400m long. There is a close correlation between the length and depth of the valleys. Crowlink, at the seaward end of Gap Bottom, is the lowest point along the Seven Sisters, hanging only

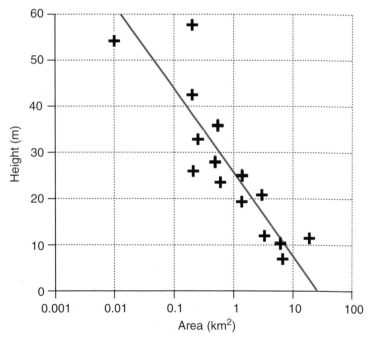

Figure 13: Pattern in the height of hanging valleys (Seven Sisters)

The larger the hanging valley's catchment area is, the lower its exit point through the Chalk cliff tends to be eroded

18m above the beach. In the eighteenth century it was possible to get down to the beach at Crowlink. It first became a centre for smuggling and later a headquarters for preventive officers; traces of the blockhouse foundations remain at the cliff edge, but cliff erosion has removed the path down to the beach.

Birling Gap marks the eastern end of the Seven Sisters. This is the last major col in the cliffline before Beachy Head and, at 12m, it is lower than any of those separating the Seven Sisters. Birling Gap represents the outfall of a significantly longer valley, The Wish, which is fed by an extensive network of dry valleys covering a total catchment area of 18km. Valleys fed by larger catchment areas tend to be eroded more deeply into the Chalk than those with smaller catchment areas. Figure 13 shows a distinct negative correlation between cliff height where the sea truncates the valley and the valley's catchment area: the Spearman rank correlation coefficient is –0.91.

The cliff below the hanging valley at Birling Gap is a natural cross-section through the periglacial deposits of coombe rock which were eroded from the Chalk backslope, probably mainly in the Devensian cold stage. Studies elsewhere show that this type of head was generated in large volumes and at rapid rates during the Devensian, and that similar material produced in earlier cold stages was mostly flushed out of the dry valleys in the early part of the Devensian. The coombe rock passes downwards into Chalk which has been shattered and heaved under periglacial conditions. The unsound Chalk passes right down to high water mark where, as at Hope Gap, its weakness facilitates marine erosion. The shore platform at Birling Gap has consequently been eroded to a lower level than to east and west, and the entire foreshore is covered by a veneer of shingle. A similar reduction of the platform is apparent at Crowlink. It may be that the fractured, weakened Chalk making up the lower cliff at Birling Gap will allow the sea to make rapid inroads and eventually open up a small cove: certainly the cliffline has retreated faster at Birling Gap than along most of the Sussex coast (see Table 3).

Table 3

Locality	Time period	Average annual loss at cliff top (metres)
Seaford Head	1973-75	0.30
Seaford Head-Beachy Head	1872-1962	0.42
Peacehaven	1973-75	0.45
Seven Sisters	1873-1962	0.51
Birling Gap	1875-1961	0.91
Birling Gap	1950-62	0.97
Birling Gap	1973-75	1.22
Seven Sisters	1973-75	1.25

The available short-term measurements show that the cliffs at Birling Gap have been retreating recently at almost exactly the same rate as the Seven Sisters. The long-term situation, however, seems to be that Birling Gap is retreating 80% faster than the Seven Sisters. The choice of timescale is all important, since cliff retreat tends to be jerky. Detailed observation of the cliff top at Birling Gap by V.J. May (May 1971) between 1950 and 1962 showed that retreat proceeds by a complex sequence of separate collapses in small lenses or narrow strips, 87% of the lost area going in winter. Observation over longer periods would doubtless show that the largest losses are widely separated in time. These catastrophic retreats are poorly recorded but it is known that in a single cliff fall in 1925 at Baily's Brow an estimated half million tons of chalk dropped onto the foreshore, producing a minor earth tremor.

There is no undercliff between Cuckmere Haven and Beachy Head, proving the efficiency of marine erosion in clearing the enormous volumes of chalk rubble supplied by cliff falls. In fact, it is basal undercutting which explains the sheer vertical form of the cliff face, and the frequency of cliff falls which explains its dazzling whiteness. Cliffs of the Seven Sisters type retreat by a combination of undercutting by wave action and the opening of joint-guided fissures within the Chalk parallel to the cliff face. The upper cliff face tends to lean seawards under gravity, because the dip is seaward, and tensional fissures are opened up. As the upper cliff fails, shear fissures are rapidly developed behind the lower cliff, so that an entire cliff face may collapse almost simultaneously.

The shore platform fronting the Seven Sisters has a steep average seaward slope of 1.5°, gradient correlating very closely (r = +0.92) with tidal range. The platform is identifiable for a width of about 400m, and the processes involved in its formation are complex; they include abrasion by the small amount of beach material, wave shock, hydraulic action (the compression of air in crevices) and solution. Cyclical wetting and drying of chalk due to the tides also causes the rock to disintegrate. In addition there is subaerial weathering: when low tides coincide with very low night-time winter temperatures (-20°C has been known) the exposed wet Chalk may be severely frost-damaged. The morning after one of these events, up to 5% of the platform area was seen to have flaked off in spalls up to 2cm thick. Bio-erosion has a major effect too. The boring piddock drill holes about 1cm in diameter into the Chalk, aiding the processes of abrasion and hydraulic action. Several of the processes accentuate the local relief of the platform, picking out joints and bedding planes: pebbles trapped in depressions tend to be 'milled' at particular spots producing pot-holes, micro-scarps (where bedding planes outcrop roughly parallel to high water mark) and deep gutters (along joints running at right angles to the shore).

The head of the shore platform is, unusually, actually below the high water mark, probably because of the high energy wave action: the altitude of this break of slope varies by as much as 4m in southern England. Shore platforms were first recognised as landforms in their own right in the nineteenth century and for a long time there was a dispute as to whether the processes forming them could be capable of producing the extensive inland erosion surfaces the geomorphologists of the first half of the twentieth century were fond of identifying. It seems likely, now that we know sea level has continually oscillated up and down during the last 2 million years, that large areas of the seabed were eroded under the same conditions as the present Seven Sisters shore platform. In fact, large areas of the central and eastern English Channel seafloor may turn out to be a composite shore platform created by the repeatedly rising and falling sea level. The submarine landscape is not like the subaerial landscape of south-east England: there are no submerged escarpments or other high-relief forms, not even domed interfluves, only a very gently sloping rock floor with a network of shallow river valleys scored across it. The low ridges separating the valleys appear to have been truncated, probably by the shore platform-eroding processes.

Access

The Seven Sisters may be approached from the west or the east. The path south from Exceat Barn car park leads diagonally onto Cliff End and from there along to Birling Gap, where there is also occasional access to the beach by a temporary scaffolding stairway. The gate at the top of the stairway is often locked to prevent visitors from getting down onto the beach: this is done in the interests of safety. There are useful information boards beside the gate.

Beachy Head

The magnificent cliffline at Beachy Head displays three different types of Chalk cliff corresponding to the three main facets of the headland. The south-facing section from Beltout to TQ 582953 has vertical cliffs of the Seven Sisters type rising to 125m at the eastern end; it is, in effect, a section through the upper part of the Chalk back slope.

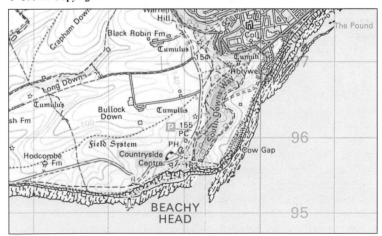

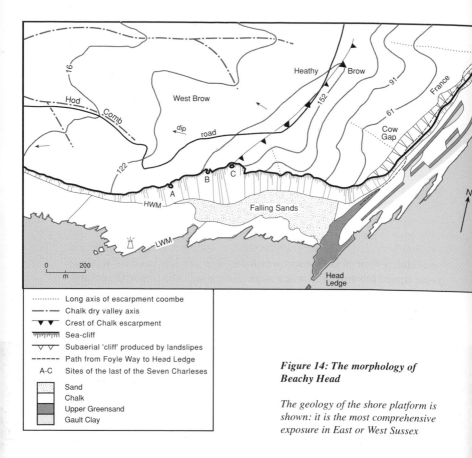

Long axis of escarpment coombe
Chalk dry valley axis
Crest of Chalk escarpment
Sea-cliff
Subaerial 'cliff' produced by landslides
Path from Foyle Way to Head Ledge
A-C   Sites of the last of the Seven Charleses

Sand
Chalk
Upper Greensand
Gault Clay

Figure 14: The morphology of Beachy Head

The geology of the shore platform is shown: it is the most comprehensive exposure in East or West Sussex

The south-south-east-facing section (TA 582953-594955) rises to 160m and cuts right through the South Downs escarpment. Along the cliff crest, tensional fissures and sand-filled solution pipes can be seen; at TQ 590955 a cross-section through an escarpment gully shows as a 4m-deep lens of yellowish coombe rock. The form of this cliff face is unusual: a vertical upper segment gives way to a middle, vegetated segment sloping at 60°, which in turn gives way to a steep (80°) bare rock lower segment. The middle segment is evidently a shear plane following a subsidiary diagonal joint: a similar feature is seen at the western end of Seaford Head. The lowest segment represents a recent modification in which tensional fissures have followed vertical joints.

Vertical pinnacles once projected from the middle segment to the level of the cliff top. These joint-controlled outliers from the main cliffline have been referred to as stacks but, since they developed two-thirds of the way up the cliff face, they should be called pinnacles or turrets. Known as The Seven Charleses, they collapsed one by one, presumably contributing to the temporary rubble of the undercliff. The last is reputed to have fallen in 1853, but three of the Charleses still survive on the 1875 maps. The cliff top is currently retreating at an average rate of 1.1m/year.

The third facet of Beachy Head (TQ 594955-602970) has a more complicated geomorphology (Figure 14). Although the cliffline rises to 155m (Heathy Brow), only the lowest quarter of this owes anything to coastal processes. The upper slopes are part of the Chalk escarpment, here facing east-south-east shaped by subaerial processes and just coincidentally next to the sea. They carry two escarpment coombes, Cow Gap and Whitbread Hole, both formed by solifluction and meltwater erosion under periglacial conditions. Whitbread Hole is a broad amphitheatre with a gently sloping floor hanging 24m above the beach. While some escarpment coombes were formed rapidly in the late Devensian, Cow Gap is lined with cold stage deposits, identified from the mollusc shells they contain, and may have been eroded earlier, perhaps in the early or middle Devensian.

The shore platform beneath the third facet is carved across the Gault Clay and Upper Greensand. Since the Gault Clay is weak, undercutting along this cliffline has been accompanied by repeated slip faulting. At each slip, a strip of Greensand was lowered to sea level and its bedding plane tipped towards high water mark. As a result, the Upper Greensand outcrop is repeated five times on the foreshore, each outcrop forming a

Photo 5: Beachy Head seen from Falling Sands. *Rising 160m above sea level, these are the highest sea-cliffs in south-east England. Photo: Rodney Castleden.*

Photo 6: Detail of the landward end of Head Ledge
These are the uppermost layers of the Upper Greensand; the Chalk rests on top to the right (west). Photo: Rodney Castleden.

steep-sided ridge; the sea has eroded them selectively to produce some bizarre fretwork. The largest exposure of Upper Greensand on the foreshore forms the jutting reef of Head Ledge (see Photo 6). As with the Chalk, wave action has picked out the bedding planes and joints to produce a local relief of up to 1.5m.

Along the western crest of the lower cliff, large slipped masses of Chalk can be seen: they have been lowered progressively towards the beach as the supporting Gault Clay has been undermined by the sea. Further east, the landslides are more confused and broken, forming a chaotic and unstable perched undercliff.

The highest points in the cliffs at Beachy Head are made of Upper Chalk: along the high water mark at Cow Gap the base of the Lower Chalk can be seen. Nearly the entire Chalk formation is on view here. It is worth remembering that some of the upper layers of the Lower Chalk are up to 50% marl (i.e. clayey and impermeable), whereas the Upper Chalk, as tested at Newhaven, is up to 98% pure calcium carbonate. Between Whitbread Hole and Holywell Steps, the 3m thick Plenus Marl layer outcrops along the foot of the cliff, throwing out several small springs about 2m above high water mark.

Access

The cliff top is easily accessible by road. The nearest road access to the cliff foot is on the B2103 (TQ 600972). Foyle Way, the footpath south, passes through Whitbread Hole and the landslipped chalk area, reaching the beach at Cow Gap (TQ 596957). Head Ledge is accessible (at low tide only) across the shore platform: it offers a panoramic view of the Beachy Head cliffline.

Safety

The earlier comments about safety apply equally to this notoriously dangerous cliff. Of the 20 or 25 people who die at Beachy Head every year, some at least fall to their deaths through sheer carelessness, walking too close to the cliff edge. **Always keep at least 3m back from the cliff edge.**

LANGNEY POINT AND THE CRUMBLES

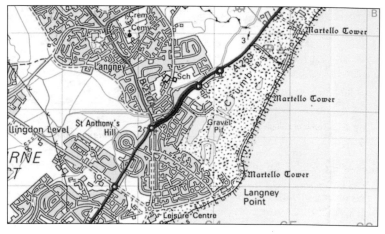

The Crumbles are an insignificant-looking diamond-shaped accumulation of beach sediment 3.5km long and 1km wide (Figure 15). Part of the landform's interest lies in its resemblance to Dungeness: it is much smaller and Langney Point, the headland developed halfway along it, is more feebly developed than Dungeness, but it may be seen as an 'immature' cuspate foreland of the same type. It consists of an almost flat expanse of shingle composed of a series of 65 parallel ridges (or 'fulls'), each representing a growth stage in the complex; they run almost exactly parallel to the east-facing shore. Most of the sediment is made of flint, probably eroded out of the Chalk outcrop immediately to the west, but there is also some chert from the Upper Greensand. The larger stones tend to be found in the west, the smaller in the east, probably a reflection of the higher energy levels on the more exposed south-facing coast. The composition of the beach has been contaminated by ship ballast, so it is hard to distinguish natural from artificial erratics: The Crumbles contain material from the Budleigh Salterton Pebble Bed and other rocks from Devon.

Traditional explanations use longshore drift to bring material eroded from Beachy Head along in front of Eastbourne to build a spit across the entrance to Pevensey Bay, eventually forming a baymouth bar. Shingle eroded from the south-western ends of the fulls is carried round Langney Point and along to the east, although not deposited immediately to the east of the point. A line of 14 Martello Towers was built on the coastline during the Napoleonic Wars; five towers on the southern shore (nos. 68-72 on Figure 15) have been destroyed by marine erosion, while the

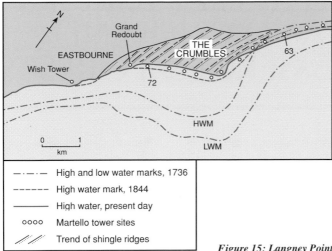

Figure 15: Langney Point

sites of the five at the eastern end of The Crumbles have been separated from the sea by an accretion of 100m of beach material.

During the accumulation of The Crumbles, the tidal water of Pevensey Bay was cut off from the sea. The resulting still-water lagoon silted rapidly and was easy to reclaim in the Middle Ages. The promontory on which the Roman-Norman Pevensey Castle was built originally had tidal water on both sides, but as the mudflats were reclaimed, the ramifying network of tidal creeks was reduced to a few embanked channels such as Pevensey Haven (TQ 6405) and Old Haven (TQ 6506). One of the tidal channels, known as 'Godyngeshaven' or 'Coding', was kept open to enable small vessels to reach Northeye, which in the Middle Ages was a limb of the Cinque Ports but is now deserted. Accounts of the 1287 flood, which wrought havoc in Romney Marsh as well, indicate that at that time nearly all of the Pevensey levels had been reclaimed. The large tidal inlet may have disappeared in as little as 200 years; this may argue for a relatively late and rapid growth of The Crumbles.

The map evidence also suggests very recent growth. Langney Point is not shown on a 1576 map, but was well developed by 1736: in fact by 1736 there was a foreland extending 1.5km further to the south of the present position of Langney Point. Since then, if the maps are accurate, the area of The Crumbles has been halved. The fact that the summits of the subdued fulls are all at the same height indicates that they were all built with the sea at its present level. It may be that this is a rapidly forming landform, one that undergoes periodic or cyclic change, and that its inability to sustain growth out into the Channel is related to the width of the Channel.The fetch of easterly and south-easterly winds at Langney Point is 90-100km, twice that at Dungeness, and it is this that has inhibited growth.

Access

There are car parks close to the sea front at the southern end of The Crumbles (TQ 625000); it is possible to walk from here to Langney Point.

GALLEY HILL AND CLIFF END SUBMERGED FORESTS

These two foreshore sites, 13km apart, carry small remnants of the great deciduous forest which covered much of the Weald 6000 years ago.

Galley Hill (TQ 758076) is, at 20m, the highest point in a low cliffline eroded in the Ashdown Beds; these are yellow sandstones resting on grey and red clays. Of geological interest are the three faults which displace the beds to the west, symptomatic of the structural complexity of the Weald. In the Glyne Gap (TQ 760079) the sandstone is eroded almost to sea level, possibly assisted by a fourth fault. To the east is the low sandstone cliff of Little Galley Hill. On the foreshore here the sea has exhumed fossilised iguanodon footprints in the sandstone bedding planes. Coincidentally, this was a foreshore 135 million years ago: in the meantime a maximum of 1600m of sediment has accumulated, hardened into rock and been removed by erosion.

On the foreshore in front of Little Galley Hill, the shore platform eroded in Fairlight Clay carries a fine example of a submerged forest. Many blackened, carbonised tree trunks lie on the shore platform: some still have their root systems and stand in their growth positions. This is not a remnant of the tropical forest inhabited by the iguanodon but a much later deciduous forest which was engulfed during the Flandrian sea level rise.

It is likely that the Galley Hill and Cliff End submerged forests were living at the same time. The Ashdown Beds cliffline at Cliff End (TQ 887130) is 20m high, made of strongly jointed sandstone. Patient geologists have found Cretaceous plant fragments, iguanodon footprints, reptile bones and some of the earliest known mammal bones.

Stretching along the grey clay foreshore north-east from Cliff End is an outcrop of black peat 0.6m thick, ragged and eroded along its seaward edge. The peat contains well-preserved leaves, twigs and branches of oak and hazel, with many tree boles still in their growth position with roots penetrating into the grey clay: some of the leaves are still green. Radiocarbon dating shows that the forest was growing 4000-4100 calendar years BC and neolithic flint tools found in the peat support this date. It is thought that the forest was engulfed by an advancing beach deposit. As the shingle has been driven further landwards, associated with the rising sea level, the forest remains – now compacted into peat – have re-emerged on the seaward side.

Access

For Little Galley Hill there is a car park next to the pedestrian tunnel under the railway line (TQ 764079). For Cliff End, there is roadside parking at Cliff End itself or along the coast road fronting Pett Level. The temptation to break off pieces of the submerged forest should be resisted. This is a Site of Special Scientific Interest (SSSI) and as such is protected by law.

DUNGENESS AND THE ROTHER MOUTH

Dungeness

Dungeness is the largest (about 250km^2) and most controversial landform on the Sussex-Kent coast, consisting of a complex of shingle ridges on the south- and east-facing coasts confining a huge expanse of marshland between them and a line of Weald Clay and Hastings Beds fossil cliffs. Dungeness has been the subject of heated debate among historians, geologists, engineers, geomorphologists and archaeologists, all working from different premises and data and all arriving at partial explanations. It is unlikely that the full story has yet emerged, particularly since the feature represents the outcome of four distinct but complicated and interrelated sets of processes: the accumulation of the shingle ridges, the deposition of silt by rivers, changes in sea level, and the role of people in turning the marshes into dry land.

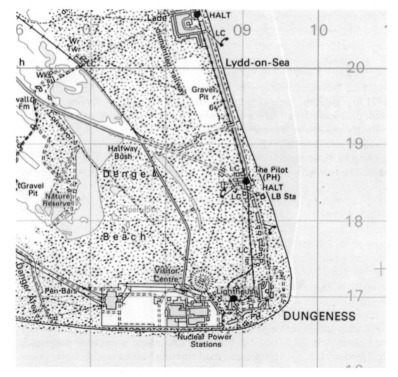

The initial stage in the foreland's development was the formation of a large bay by the postglacial sea level rise. Sea-cliffs trimmed back at this time (around 4000 BC) are clearly visible as a conspicuous line of steep grassy scarps 30-40m high, curving north-eastwards from Cliff End to Hythe with breaks where the Rivers Brede, Tillingham and Rother emptied into the bay. Earlier explanations of Dungeness place great emphasis on longshore drift carrying sediment eroded from Hastings and Fairlight into the bay, whereas it is likely that the initial coating of coarse sand was the result partly of (Hastings Beds) cliff erosion in the bay, partly of the onshore movement of sand from the seabed. The result of these two contrary movements seems to have been the accumulation of a string of offshore sand bars up to 2km wide, extending from TQ 9816 to TQ 0928 about 8-9km from the coast. Consolidated by onshore drift, these may have evolved into barrier islands. Although this sand (the Midley Sand) is covered by 5m of more recent shingle, the 20m thick layer still has a detectable influence on the surface landscape, showing as south-west–north-east-aligned islands rising 3m above the ground level of the marsh at New Romney, Jack's Court near Lydd and Mydley in the Walland Marsh.

From 2000 BC onwards, in the sheltered bay behind the sand bars, silt accumulated rapidly. The rivers entering the bay drained areas that were being cleared for agriculture and may be assumed to have carried large quantities of soil eroded from Bronze Age fields by rain and plough. In places this accumulated to sea level in the bay, allowing a woodland cover to develop. Two further factors in the development of this focus of deposition may be (1) the shelter from the prevailing west-south-west winds provided by the cliffs at Fairlight, and (2) wave refraction. Wave fronts driven from the west-south-west would have been refracted round into the bay in such a way as to create a very steep energy gradient, energy levels dropping dramatically as the wave fronts entered the bay. This may have led to massive deposition where extension of wave fronts took energy levels below a critical threshold. Meanwhile, shingle beaches were built onto the seaward fringes of the sand bars, possibly once again as a result of onshore drift.

Colonisation by land plants (a woodland of birch, hazel, alder) was terminated by a rise in water level and the resulting peat layer was sealed by a layer of alluvium. The western parts of the silting bay (Walland Marsh) seem to have remained higher or to have emerged thanks to a slight lowering of sea level, and by the close of the Romano-British period (AD 300-400) they were crossed by streams making for a large tidal inlet on the site of Romney Marsh connecting with the sea at Hythe. By this time the offshore sand and shingle bars were probably strung together, and linked to the mainland at Fairlight, by longshore drift and onshore drift to make a large though fragile spit 30km long (Figure 16). Eight Romano-British settlements are known to have existed on the landward edge of the spit, so the adjacent areas of the marsh must already have been stable and drying out.

At some stage, perhaps early in the Saxon period, the spit was breached at Romney and Rye. This may have been caused by a slight rise in sea level, but it is more probably a normal side-effect of spit formation; variations in longshore drift may cause beach starvation and critical local

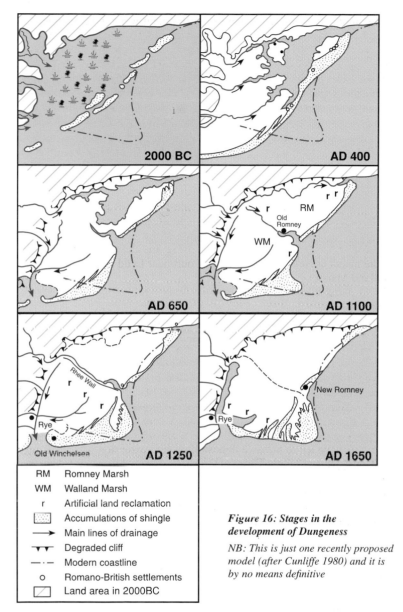

RM	Romney Marsh
WM	Walland Marsh
r	Artificial land reclamation
	Accumulations of shingle
→	Main lines of drainage
⊤⊤	Degraded cliff
—·—	Modern coastline
o	Romano-British settlements
	Land area in 2000BC

Figure 16: Stages in the development of Dungeness

NB: This is just one recently proposed model (after Cunliffe 1980) and it is by no means definitive

thinning of a spit: the same waves that produce an onshore movement of sediment may also cause breaching. Cyclical breaching of this kind is known from Christchurch Harbour in Dorset, and is suspected from what is known of Pagham Harbour in Sussex. The Rye breach and the associated flooding of what is now East Guldeford Level seem to have resulted in the capture (i.e. reorientation) of the Brede and the Tillingham: from now on these rivers flowed southwards to empty into Rye Bay. The diversion of this water may have had profound effects on the northern estuary, where silting would have been rapid, so that by AD 1100 – with human help – the reclamation and settlement of Romney Marsh was complete. According to one view (Cunliffe 1980) the Romney breach captured no through-drainage at first, but created its own local net of tidal creeks, an estuary that became Romney Hoy, the harbour of New Romney; this grew by headward extension during tidal surges until, some time later, it diverted water from the northern channel of the Rother (as shown in Figure 16). Another, more recent, view (Green 1988) is that the Rother never flowed eastwards from Appledore to Hythe but instead looped southwards into Walland Marsh before flowing north-eastwards immediately behind the shingle barrier, past the site of Old Romney, to approach the Hythe estuary from the south-west. The Romney breach could, in this scenario, have captured the Rother's water straight away and led to rapid silting in the Hythe inlet.

The sequence in the Walland Marsh is still less clear. The Rhee Wall, the precise date of which is not known, may have been built in about AD 1250, after the Romney channel captured a significant flow of water from the Rother: only then would it have become a significant landform. The Rhee Wall may have been built to contain the water in this channel and thereby keep a waterway open from Appledore to Romney, or simply to provide a flow of water that would keep Romney Harbour open. According to Green (1988), the Rhee Wall and its accompanying channel did not follow the line of a natural river channel at all, but cut right across the early course of the Rother. To the south, the system of silting tidal creeks in the Walland Marsh was still emptying via the Brede-Tillingham estuary into Rye Bay, although the higher areas were embanked and drained by 1400.

Meanwhile the protecting barrier of the shingle spit had changed its shape. Between Rye Bay and New Romney it had begun to develop its distinctive cuspate form, elbowing out into the Channel. Sediment eroded from its south-facing shore was transferred round the headland and deposited on the east-facing shore, a process that continues today. The destruction along the southern shore had its inevitable human impact. Old Winchelsea (just south of Camber?) was so badly damaged by storms in 1250 and 1287 that it had to be abandoned: New Winchelsea was built on top of an abandoned cliff 6km to the west. The 1287 storm surge swept into the southern estuary, redistributing a great deal of sediment and finally capturing the northern branch of the Rother. This enlargement of Rye's tidal compartment ensured the future success of the port of Rye: the loss of the Rother and the accretion of coastal shingle on the east coast ensured that Romney was finished as a port.

The story from the medieval period on has been one of continued silting at Rye and New Romney, and the reorientation of the coastline, the Ness (point) itself advancing at a rate of about 1m/year east-south-eastwards into the Channel. The survival, indeed growth, of this huge headland in what would appear to be a hostile environment requires some explanation. Early ideas that Dungeness marked the meeting place of east and south coast tides or eastward and southward longshore drift must be rejected. Nevertheless, a new computer-generated model showing tide-generated stress vectors on the seabed (Austin 1991) indicates the likely sand transport paths; Dungeness is in a 'slack' area between an eastward drift from between the Isle of Wight and Cherbourg and a strong south-westward drift through the Straits of Dover, a location favouring sediment accumulation. An important factor in creating and maintaining the sharpness of the foreland is the narrowness of the Channel. Powerful storm waves come either from the east-north-east through the Dover Strait with a fetch of 700km or from the west-south-west from the Atlantic with a fetch of up to 7000km. Waves approaching from directly across the Channel, from the east, east-south-east or south-east, have a short fetch, only 45-50km, and are correspondingly impotent; the weakness of waves from those directions has allowed Dungeness to grow out towards the east-south-east.

The growth rate nevertheless slows down as the Ness builds out into comparatively deep water. Meanwhile, the reclaimed marshes forming the bulk of the foreland are perilously low-lying: The Dowels, near Appledore (TQ 9830), are only a metre above present sea level. Dungeness is sinking at a rate of 1mm/year as a result of the general crustal subsidence at the southern end of the North Sea. Added to this is the sea level rise affecting the whole of the Sussex coast at a rate of about 1mm/year (1900-82); this is likely to increase to 8-25mm/year during the period 1996-2100. How Dungeness will fare in the face of a sea level rise of between 1m and 3m in the next 100 years will hinge on the supply of sediment; along the Sussex coast as a whole much will depend on sediment supply being sufficient to allow beach-building to keep pace with the rising sea.

The Rother Mouth

During the last 300 years the mouth of the Rother has suffered a similar fate to the Hythe and Romney outlets: it has become progressively choked with sediment as a result of a combination of fluvial silting and marine deposition. After Old Winchelsea was overwhelmed (around 1300) a large bay existed here. Shingle ridges were built successively against its western coast, possibly as the recurved ends of a spit rooted at Cliff End.

Camber Castle seems to have been built close to the shoreline (in 1538); a map dated 1594 shows the coast only 230m away to the east. By 1698 the accumulation of shingle ridges had moved the coastline another 300m east of the castle, and the pattern for the next 300 years was established. A Martello Tower marks the mouth of the Rother in 1804: since then, the outfall has been moved over a kilometre seawards by the accumulating shingle.

The mouth of the Rother has to be kept open by a harbour groyne; the build-up on the west side of the groyne clearly shows that the longshore drift on Winchelsea Beach is from west to east. On Camber Sands, to the east of the Rother mouth, there is persistent beach starvation and longshore drift is locally reversed; as far east as Broomhill (TQ 975182) there is a westward drift, probably a result of the shelter created by the

© Crown Copyright

projecting harbour groyne – the same effect as seen in the lee of Newhaven breakwater.

The older shingle ridges (e.g. The Nook) have been extensively quarried. The wisdom of removing large quantities of sediment from temporary stores in a delicately balanced system is questionable. Removing sand and shingle from the seabed off the Sussex coast, as it has been, in millions of tonnes, is worse and may prove to be disastrous, since it would now seem that beaches, bars and spits have been supplied to a great extent from this offshore zone, and well-nourished beaches offer far and away the best defence against the power of the sea.

Access

There is roadside parking at TQ 911153 for Winchelsea Beach, and TQ 972184-987181 for Camber and Broomhill Sands and a view along the south coast of Dungeness. A road network covers the whole of Dungeness and there is informal roadside parking at the Ness itself, between the two lighthouses (TR 092168).

GLOSSARY

Anticline An upward fold in the rock layers.

Back slope or **Dip slope** The gentler slope of a ridge of hills which follows the geological dip of the underlying rock layers.

BP The date in years before present; 'bp' indicates uncorrected radiocarbon date.

Coombe rock A chalky sediment which was formed by alternate freezing and thawing in cold (i.e. periglacial) stages of the Ice Age. Chalk disintegrated by freeze-thaw action was moved down the valley sides and along the valley bottoms by solifluction and by summer snowmelt.

Cuspate delta A delta is an accumulation of river sediment deposited where the river enters the sea or a lake. A cuspate delta is more or less triangular with the apex of the triangle pointing out into the sea (or lake). It has been suggested that the cuspate form is due to the domination of wave energy over the other two key environmental factors, river processes and tides.

Devensian The name of the last cold stage of the Ice Age, lasting from about 110 000 years ago to 10 000 years ago. A great deal of the detail of the present land surface of Sussex was modelled during the Devensian.

Discordant A term denoting a land surface or a drainage pattern whose form is at variance with the underlying rock structure.

Erratic A stone or pebble whose rock type is not found locally in the solid rock layers. An erratic can only have been introduced into an area by processes which are no longer operating.

Floodplain The nearly flat valley floor which borders a river. It is regularly overflowed by the river and is composed of sediment deposited by the river.

Glacio-eustatic oscillations Eustatic movements are worldwide changes in sea level. These may result from distortions in the earth's crust which cause the capacity of the ocean basins to change. Glacio-eustatic changes, however, result from changes in the amount of water in the oceans; this varies according to the volume of water stranded on the continents in the form of glaciers and ice sheets. During cold stages, when a lot of water is locked up in glaciers and ice sheets, sea level may drop 100m or more below its warm stage level.

Interglacial A warm stage: an episode of some 10 000-20 000 years during which the climate is approximately as warm as today.

Ipswichian The name of the last interglacial or warm stage of the Ice Age, lasting from about 130 000 to 110 000 years ago.

Loess A fine dust or silt carried, sometimes long distances, by winds blowing from the margins of an ice sheet. Periglacial regions, or regions which were once periglacial, are often coated with loess.

Longshore drift The gradual, piecemeal movement of pebbles, shingle and sand along the beach in one direction as a result of many repeated (though individually small) swash and backwash movements. On the Sussex coast, longshore drift is from west to east at nearly every point, because the most frequent strong onshore winds (= dominant winds) are westerlies and they drive the waves eastwards.

Notch The break of slope marking the landward end of the shore platform, or the junction between the shore platform and the cliff. It usually develops at the high water mark.

Onshore drift The gradual landward movement of sediment from seabed to beach. It results from a combination of piecemeal wave action and a long-term rise in sea level (e.g. 10 000-5000 BP). The process must have accompanied the onset of each interglacial.

Periglacial A term relating to a near-glacial environment, frozen and snow-covered for up to ten months every year, thawing for only two or three.

Piddock A boring mollusc.

Raised beach A group of shoreline features left stranded after a fall in sea level. The raised beach may, if well preserved, consist of a degraded cliff and a shore platform coated with ancient beach deposits.

Rejuvenation Renewed downcutting by rivers in response to a drop in sea level. This traditional view of the relationship between river behaviour and sea level is now questioned by some geomorphologists.

Scarp slope The steeper slope of a ridge of hills.

Shore platform A low-angle erosional bench cut almost horizontally across the solid rock by wave action. Although unnoticed by many visitors, it is really the primary landform produced by marine erosion.

Syncline A downward fold in the rock layers.

Tombolo A bar of sand or shingle connecting an island to the mainland.

Undercliff The loose rock debris produced by cliff falls or landslides: it accumulates at the foot of the cliff. The undercliff is usually fairly temporary, since wave action clears the debris away.

BIBLIOGRAPHY

Anon (1977) *Report on the problems of coastal erosion*. East Sussex County Planning Office.

Austin, R.M. (1991) 'Modelling Holocene tides on the North-West European continental shelf' in *Terra Nova*, 3, 276-88.

Castleden, R. (1975) 'The origin of Chalk dry valleys: an interpretation of the South Downs' in *Croydon Natural History and Scientific Society*, 16, 28-34.

Cunliffe, B.W. (1980) 'The evolution of Romney Marsh: a preliminary statement' in Thompson, F.H. (ed) *Archaeology and coastal change*. Society of Antiquaries, 37-55.

Curry, D. (1989) 'The rock floor of the English Channel and its significance for interpretation of marine unconformities' in *Proceedings of the Geologists' Association*, 100, 339-52.

Davies, K.H. and Keen, D.H. (1985) 'The age of Pleistocene marine deposits at Portland, Dorset' in *Proceedings of the Geologists' Association*, 96, 217-25.

Doornkamp, J. (1990) *The greenhouse effect and rising sea levels in the UK*. M1 Press, Nottingham.

Gibbon, W. (1981) *The Weald*. Unwin, London.

Gilbert, C.J. (1933) 'The evolution of Romney Marsh' in *Archaeologia Cantiana*, 45, 246-72.

Green, C. (1988) 'Palaeogeography of marine inlets in the Romney Marsh area' in Eddison, J. and Green, C.P. (eds), *Romney Marsh: evolution, occupation, reclamation*. Oxford Committee for Archaeology Monograph no. 24, 167-74.

Hodgson, J.M. (1964) 'The low-level Pleistocene marine sands and gravels of the West Sussex coastal plain' in *Proceedings of the Geologists' Association*, 75, 547-61.

Jones, D.K.C. (1980) *The shaping of southern England*. Academic Press, London.

Jones, D.K.C. (1981) *Southeast and southern England*. Methuen, London.

May, V.J. (1971) 'The retreat of Chalk cliffs' in *Geographical Journal*, 137, 203-6.

Milner, H.B. and Bull, A.J. (1925) 'The geology of the Eastbourne-Hastings coastline' in *Proceedings of the Geologists' Association*, 36, 291-314.

Smith, A.J. (1989) 'The English Channel – geological design or catastrophic accident?' in *Proceedings of the Geologists' Association*, 100, 325-37.